THE SUMMER BEFORE...

FIRST GRADE

English

Helping your child

- Remember that the activities in this book should be enjoyed by your child. Try to find a quiet place to work.

- Your child does not need to complete each page in one sitting. Always stop before your child gets tired, and come back to the same page another time.

- It is important to work through the pages in the right order because the activities get progressively more difficult.

- When you see a paint splat (❀) your child should name the color of the splat when doing the activity.

- The answers to the activities begin on page 120.

- Always give your child a lot of encouragement and praise.

- Use the stickers to reward effort as well as achievement. Put a star sticker on the page when each activity has been completed.

Written by David and Penny Glover, Betty Root, Monica Hughes,
Paul Broadbent, and Peter Patilla.
Text and artwork copyright © 2002 by Parragon Books Ltd.
This 2011 edition published by Sandy Creek,
by arrangement with Parragon.

Sandy Creek
387 Park Avenue South
New York, NY 10016

ISBN 978-1-4351-3432-4

Printed in Guangzhou
Manufactured 03/07/2012
Lot 10 9 8 7 6 5 4 3 2

THE SUMMER BEFORE...

FIRST GRADE

English

Sandy Creek

Contents

Contents

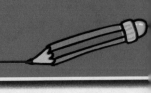

Color the words

Color the words that you can read.

a	am	and
at	all	are
away	big	can
come	cat	day
dog	dad	for
go	going	get
he	I	it

Note for parent: Many children will still be learning these words.
Practice reading, writing, and spelling them.

is	in	look
like	mom	me
my	no	of
on	play	said
she	see	to
the	this	they
up	we	was
went	you	yes

Writing the alphabet

Trace over the guides to write each letter in the rocket.

Write your name here:

Note for parent: Remind your child that names begin with a capital letter.

Trace over the guides to write the capital letters in the stars.

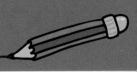

A
a

B
b

C
c

D
d

E
e

F
f

G
g

H
h

I
i

J
j

K
k

L
l

M
m

N
n

O
o

P
p

Q
q

R
r

S
s

T
t

U
u

V
v

W
w

X
x

Y
y

Z
z

11

Spot the sound

Say the name of each thing.
Circle the sound in the middle of each name.

Note for parent: Emphasize the middle sounds as you say the words with your child.

Double sounds

Say these double sounds. Choose the right one to start each word. Write it in the spaces.

cl sp fl gr tr sn

ee

_ _

ower

_ _

oon

_ _

apes

_ _

ail

_ _

ock

_ _

Note for parent: Help your child to think of some more words that begin with each of these sounds.

Umbrella words

Can you read these words?
Write sentences using some of them.

an came have man seen very
do back here name that were
be girl house not there when
boy got little our tree will
by had made ran us your

The **girl ran** to the **little house**. It was **by** a **tree**.

....

....

....

....

14

Finish the words

Say these double sounds. Choose the right one to finish each word. Write it in place.

sh ck th ng ss ch

pa _ _

fi _ _

swi _ _

wat _ _

du _ _

gra _ _

Note for parent: Emphasize the ending as you say each word.

Word sort

Count the letters in each word. Write each word in the correct box.

2-letter words	3-letter words

got
do
had
be
ran
us
trees
made
house
name
boys
girls

4-letter words	5-letter words

Can you read all of these words?

Note for parent: Writing a word reinforces knowledge of its spelling.

Color words

Read the words. Draw lines to match each color to the correct flower.

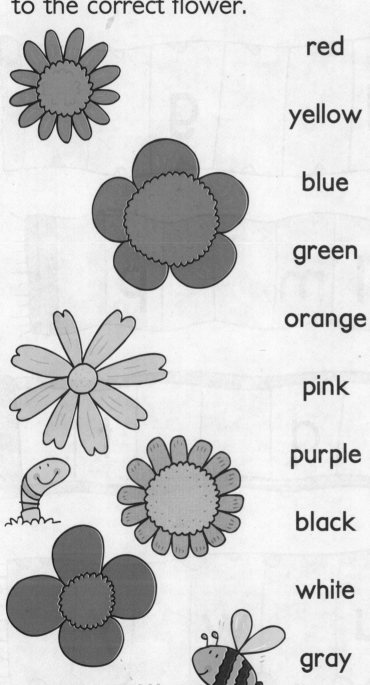

red

yellow

blue

green

orange

pink

purple

black

white

gray

In the right order

Write the missing letters on these scarves.

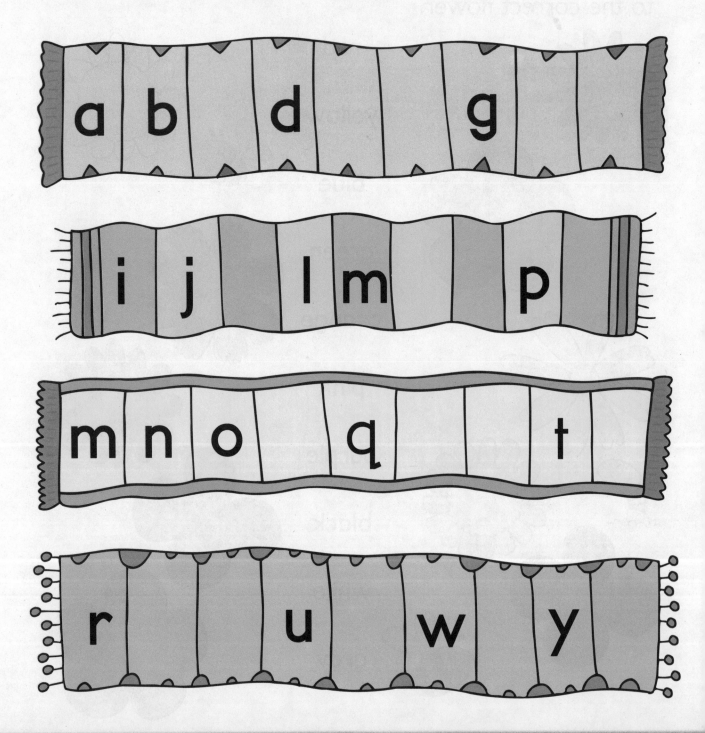

a b d g

i j l m p

m n o q t

r u w y

Note for parent: This activity practices placing letters
in alphabetical order.

Odd one out

Read the words in each row and circle the odd one out.

here	here	here	have	here

when	when	were	when	when

boy	boy	boy	by	boy

girl	got	girl	girl	girl

house	house	house	had	house

that	there	that	that	that

made	man	man	man	man

name	name	name	name	not

Note for parent: This activity helps your child recognize some high-usage everyday words.

Rhyming words

Write the rhyming words.

What moves slowly and rhymes with nail?

 _ _ _ _ _

What goes buzz and rhymes with tree?

 _ _ _

What is the cat lying on that rhymes with ball?

 _ _ _ _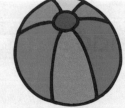

Cloud words

Can you read these words?
Use some of them to make sentences.

as	call	her	live	one
then	ball	did	him	may
over	too	bed	down	his
must	put	want	been	good
if	new	so	what	but
has	last	off	take	with

The boy **put** the **ball** under **his bed**.

Word table

Look at the first letter of each word. Write each word in the correct column in the table.

ball	what	has	him
off	want	bed	over
one	her	with	but

b	h	o	w

Note for parent: This activity teaches children to classify by initial letter. Writing the word reinforces knowledge of its spelling.

The same endings

Say these double sounds. Choose the right one to end each word. Write it in place.

ll   ed   ce   ar   og

ba _ _ _

mi _ _ _

b _ _ _

l _ _ _

c _ _ _

r _ _ _

be _ _ _

st _ _ _

di _ _ _

d _ _ _

Draw lines to connect the things that end the same way.

Note for parent: This activity introduces some common word endings.

Vowels

There are 26 letters in the alphabet. The five vowels are **a, e, i, o**, and **u**. Find the vowels on this snail. Color them in.

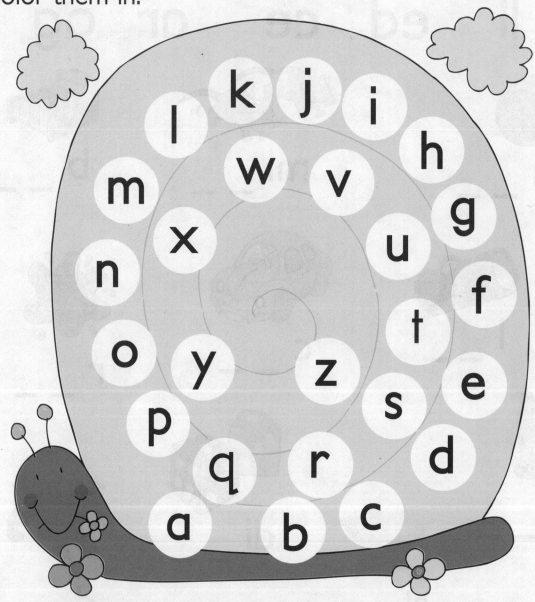

Write the five vowels here.

_____ _____ _____ _____ _____

Note for parent: Sing or say the alphabet with your child.

Consonants

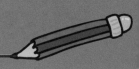

The yellow bees are carrying vowels. All the other bees are carrying consonants. Say the sound of each consonant and color in the bee carrying it.

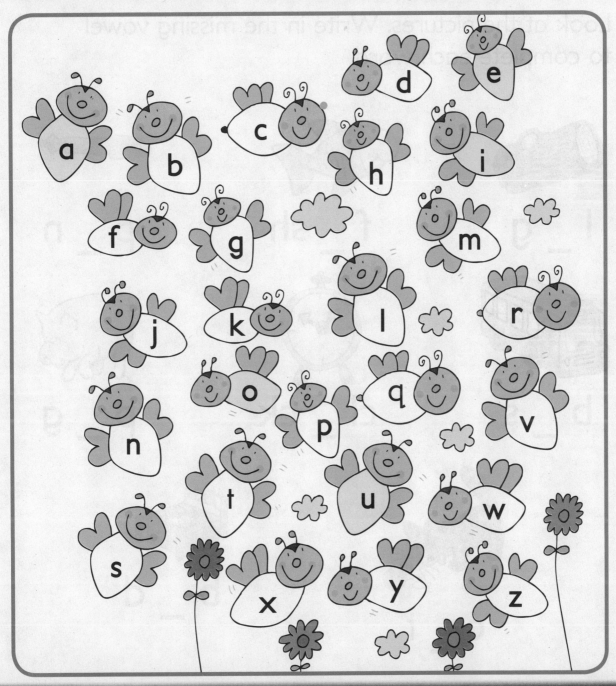

Missing vowels

Here are the five vowels.

a e i o u

Look at the pictures. Write in the missing vowel to complete each word.

l _ g   f _ sh   p _ n

b _ s   cl _ ck   p _ g

c _ t   b _ d

Can you read these words?
Use some of them to make sentences.

again   door
them   love
brother   old
push   where   can't   saw
now   school   night   help   time
or   would   should
lived   make   pull   more
dig   from   home   out
sister   could   who
about

I **love school.**

Catch a word

These nets only catch words with the right number of letters. Count the letters and draw lines to connect each word to the right net.

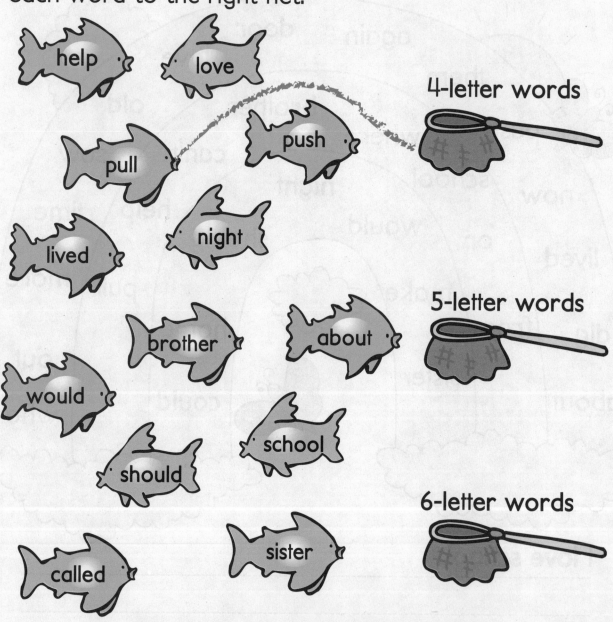

4-letter words

5-letter words

6-letter words

The nets can't catch one word because it has 7 letters. Can you find it?

Sentences

Read these sentences. Circle the capital letters and the periods.

The farmer is in his field.

Ducks can swim.

Pigs like to play in mud.

We get milk from cows.

A horse can run.

Write your own sentence here.

- -

Note for parent: Tell your child that a sentence always starts with a capital letter and ends with a period.

Missing words

Choose the right word to complete each sentence.

We go to bed at _____. | day   night |

Snowballs are _____. | hot   cold |

An elephant is _____. | light   heavy |

A baby is _____. | old   young |

A brick feels very _____. | hard   soft |

Note for parent: Discuss opposites with your child.

Question marks

Read these questions. Put a ✔ if the answer is "yes," or an ✗ if the answer is "no."

yes ✔ no ✗

Is ice cream hot? ▢

Do dogs bark? ▢

Is snow purple? ▢

Are mice small? ▢

Can you swim? ▢

Write your own question here.

_____

31

Note for parent: Tell your child that a question always starts with a capital letter and ends with a question mark.

Write it correctly

Write the words in the right order to make questions. Then put a ✔ or an ✗ to answer "yes" or "no."

yes ✔ no ✗

pink Is cat the

_____?

grass green Is

_____?

man Can fly a

_____?

frog Can croak a

_____?

Star words

Can you read these words? Color in the stars as you read each one.

after

how

another

first

because

laugh

people

half

some

called

three

than

once

their

these

water

way

just

jump

two

took

don't

much

many

next

Adding the letter e

Read each word. Add the letter **e** at the end to make a new word. Write the new word in the spaces.

 cap  _ _ _ _

 fir _ _ _ _

 cub _ _ _ _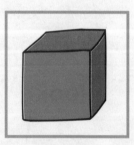

Note for parent: This activity helps your child to understand the effect of a silent e at the end of a word.

Does it belong?

Read the words in each row and circle the odd one out.

these	these	three	these	these

many	many	many	much	many

half	half	half	half	how

water	way	water	water	water

after	another	after	after	after

than	than	their	than	than

two	took	two	two	two

called	called	called	called	call

Hidden words

Find the hidden word in each row of flags. Write it in the space.

z f i r s t q w _____

x s l a u g h a _____

j u s t e a y u _____

i b e c a u s e _____

a d s j u m p b _____

Note for parent: Word searches help with spelling.

Plurals

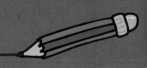

Add an **s** to make the plurals of these words.

 one apple    two <u>apples</u>

 one banana    two _____

 one orange   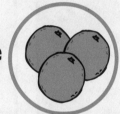 three _____

 one grape    four _____

 one pear    five _____

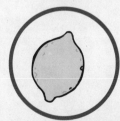 one lemon    six _____

Note for parent: Explain that plural means "more than one."

Days and months

Can you read these words?

Days of the week	Months of the year
Monday	January
Tuesday	February
Wednesday	March
Thursday	April
Friday	May
Saturday	June
Sunday	July
	August
	September
	October
	November
	December

Complete these sentences.

Today is _____.

The month is _____.

Note for parent: Ask your child about events in their life and when they happen.

Seasons

There are four seasons in the year. Write the name of the season under each picture.

> spring   summer   fall   winter

Complete these sentences with your own words.

In spring, _____ .

In summer, _____ .

In fall, _____ .

In winter, _____ .

Number words

Read the number words. Draw a line to match each word to its numeral.

zero   one   two   three   four   five

0   2   1   3   4   5

six   seven   eight   nine   ten

7   9   6   8   10

eleven   twelve   thirteen   fourteen   fifteen

12   13   15   11   14

sixteen   seventeen   eighteen   nineteen   twenty

17   19   16   18   20

Writing numbers

Write the number words for these numerals.

0 _____

2 _____

4 _____

6 _____

8 _____

10 _____

12 _____

14 _____

16 _____

18 _____

20 _____

Building words

Make the words by drawing lines to connect the parts together.

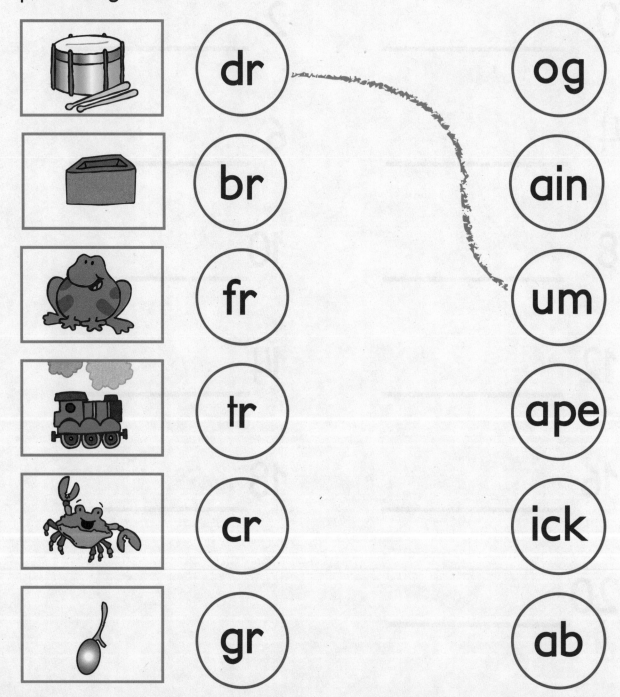

Opposites

Draw lines to connect each word to its opposite.

happy

sad

heavy

cold

full

little

hot

empty

big

light

stop

go

Note for parent: Play a "what's the opposite of _____ ?"
word game. Take turns to ask the questions.

All about me

Fill in the missing words.

My name is _____

I am _____ years old.

I live at _____

_____

_____.

My school is called _____.

My favorite animal is _____.

My favorite sport is _____.

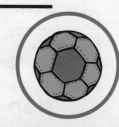

Note for parent: Giving information is a useful skill.

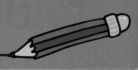

Draw yourself in the box.
Read the words and draw a line to the right part.

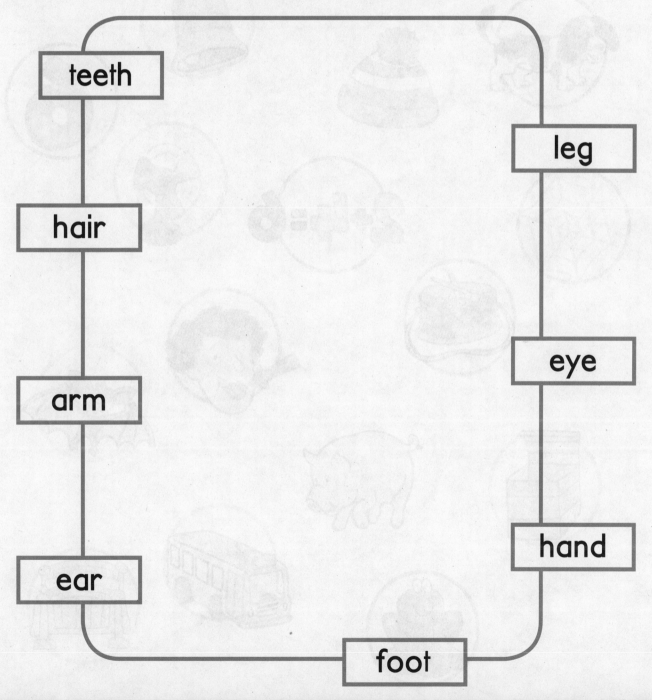

teeth

hair

arm

ear

leg

eye

hand

foot

Note for parent: This activity helps with understanding parts of the body.

Middle sounds

Connect the pictures that have the same middle sounds—**a**, **e**, **i**, **o**, or **u**.

Note for parent: Children have to listen very carefully to hear middle sounds. Be patient!

Middle vowels

Use the vowels **a**, **e**, **i**, **o**, or **u** to complete the words below.

s _ ck

m _ n

r _ d

p _ _ g

b _ s

j _ t

d _ _ ck

f _ sh

cr _ _ b

b _ d

l _ g

b _ ll

Note for parent: This activity gives children extra practice in identifying middle sounds.

Odd one out

Cross out the picture in each row that does not belong.

Silly or sensible?

Look at the picture. Read the sentences and put a check next to the ones that are sensible. Put an 'x' by the ones that are silly.

The teacher is under the table. ____
A girl is reading a book. ____
A boy is painting the door. ____
The teacher is looking at the children. ____
A cat is reading a book. ____
A boy is holding a brush. ____
The hamster is on its cage. ____

Note for parent: This activity helps children to understand sentences and make the correct response.

Using labels

Read these words:

| ball | boy | girl | man | car | tree |

Now write the words in the boxes below.

The alphabet

Write in the missing letters. Some are capital letters and some are lower-case ones.
Draw your own pictures in the empty squares.

Note for parent: This activity helps with capital letters and beginning sounds.

Double sounds

Look at these pictures and say each beginning sound.

 **bl**  **br**  **cl**  **cr**

Fill in the missing letters.

 _ _ ock  **_ _ idge**  **_ _ own** **_ _ ack**

Now do the same again.

 **dr**  **fl**  **gr**  **pl**

 **_ _ een**  **_ _ ant**  **_ _ ill**  **_ _ ag**

52

Note for parent: This activity helps children to learn these double beginning sounds: bl, br, cl, cr, dr, fl, gr, and pl.

Beginning sounds

Look at the first picture in each row.
Check the other pictures in the same
row that start with the same sound.

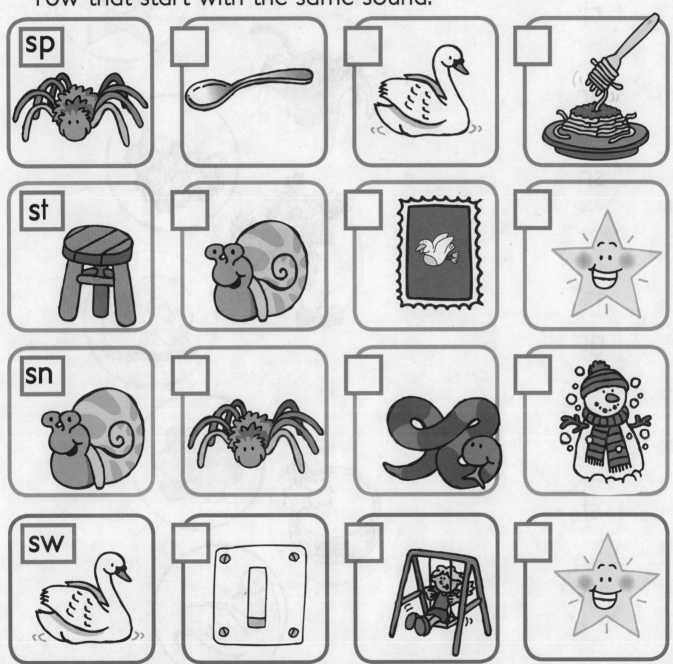

Note for parent: This activity helps children to learn these double
beginning sounds: sp, st, sn, and sw.

Second chance

Connect the sounds to the pictures.

cl

dr

sn

bl

gr

sp

st

sw

Note for parent: Here is a second chance to remember double sounds.

Read and draw

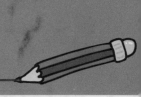

Read the sentences and finish the picture.

Draw a tree **by** the river.
Draw a boat going **under** the bridge.
Draw a duck **on** the river.
Draw a car going **over** the bridge.
Draw yourself climbing **up** the tree.

Note for parent: This activity helps children to learn positional words such as by, under, on, over, and up.

Storytime

Look at the pictures. Read the sentences.
Match each sentence to the correct picture.

Everyone fell over and the onion came out. ___

The farmer saw an enormous onion. ___

Everyone tried to pull up the onion. ___

The farmer tried to pull up the onion. ___

Note for parent: This activity gives practice in reading
for understanding.

How does it end?

Look at each row of pictures.
Tell the story but choose the
ending that you like the best.

or

or

or

Note for parent: This activity gives children practice in telling a
story from pictures.

Alphabetical order 1

a b c d e f g h i j k l m n o p q r s t u v w x y z

Write the beginning sound of each picture.
Then put the three letters in each row in
alphabetical order.

_ _ _

_ _ _

_ _ _

_ _ _

_ _ _

Note for parent: Two skills are required for this activity—
knowing beginning sounds and alphabetical order.

Little words

Find each little word in one of the big words and then connect them with a line.

or

us

an

all

am

in

at

lamb

fork

twins

bat

man

ball

bus

How many of the little words can you read? _____

Note for parent: It's a lot of fun to find words inside other words.

Find the right word

sun bed boy ball girl tree

Choose one of these words to complete each of the sentences.

A little __girl__ put on her dress.

The _____ was hot.

I like getting into my _____ to go to sleep.

I can see a bird's nest in the _____ .

Dad kicked the _____ .

A little _____ put on his baseball cap.

60

Note for parent: This activity helps children to read and understand key words.

Making sentences

These sentences are all mixed up. Write them in the correct order and then finish each one with a period (.) or a question mark (?).

is time What it

_____

chips I to like eat

_____

do go school When I to

_____

car going The was fast

_____

up Who the with went Jill hill

_____

on lap The likes sit to my cat

_____

How many capital letters can you count? ____

Note for parent: This activity gives practice with sorting words to make sense, and using punctuation.

Alphabetical order 2

Look at the names and then write them in the list in the correct order. Remember the capital letters.

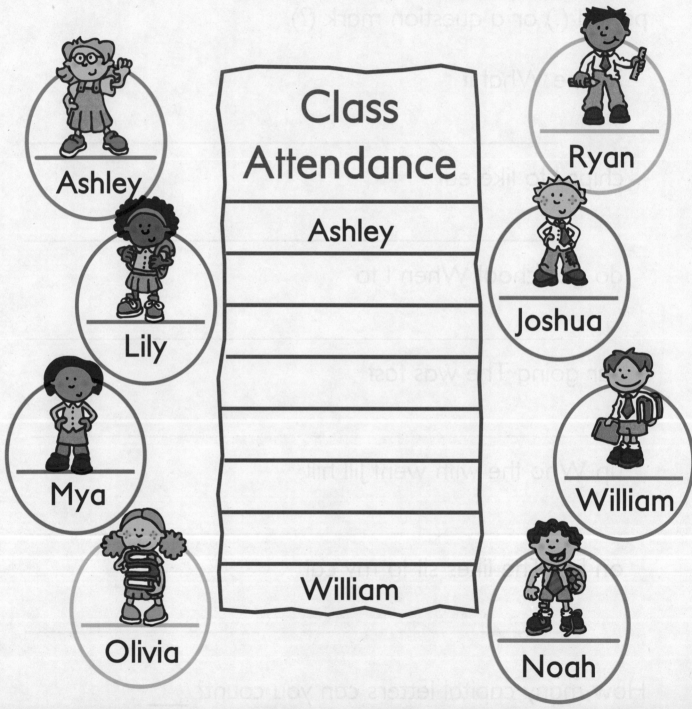

Class Attendance

Ashley

William

Note for parent: This activity helps children to practice using alphabetical order for a familiar situation.

Days of the week

Look at the pictures. Read the questions and then write the correct day. Remember the capital letters.

 Chloe

 Jack

Monday

Tuesday

Wednesday

Thursday

On which day does Chloe go trampolining? _____

On which day does Chloe watch television? _____

On which day does Jack go to the library? _____

On which day does Chloe go shopping? _____

On which day does Jack wash the car? _____

On which day does Chloe take the dog out? _____

On which day does Jack play soccer?_____

Friday

Saturday

Sunday

63

Find your way

Read these instructions. Draw the correct way from the house to the school.

Start at ✘

Walk down the path and turn right out of the gate.

Turn right again past some trees.

Walk along the sidewalk to the traffic lights.

Cross the street when it is safe.

Turn right and then turn left into **School Road**.

Go past the fence and turn left through the school gate.

Note for parent: This activity helps children to read instructions and follow them.

Telephone numbers

Use this telephone book to answer the questions at the bottom of the page.

Mr. Anderson	9802	Mr. Mead	9980
Mr. Caswell	9146	Miss Palmer	9544
Mrs. Depster	9829	Mr. Shah	9827
Miss Heelan	9026	Mrs. Todd	9412
Ms. Kamara	9530	Ms. Walker	9361

What is Mr. Shah's number? _____

What is Miss Heelan's number? _____

What is Mr. Caswell's number? _____

What is Miss Palmer's number? _____

Whose number is 9361? _____

Whose number is 9802? _____

Whose number is 9412? _____

Whose number is 9829? _____

Do you know your own
telephone number at home? _____

Note for parent: This activity helps children to learn how
to use lists of numbers.

Animal dictionary

Match each word to the correct meaning.
Draw a line to connect them.

elephant

A large animal that can jump very well. It carries its young in a pouch. It comes from Australia.

kangaroo

A small animal with long arms, and feet that it uses like hands. It lives in jungles.

monkey

A large animal with a long trunk and ivory tusks. It lives in Africa and Asia.

panda

An animal like a horse with black and white stripes. It lives in Africa.

zebra

A black and white animal like a bear. It lives in China.

Note for parent: This activity helps children to learn how to use a dictionary.

Reading an index

Use the index below to answer the questions at the bottom of the page.

Index

apes	10	kangaroos	20
bears	8	monkeys	6
chimpanzees	14	penguins	28
crocodiles	22	sharks	4
dolphins	26	turtles	12
giraffes	18	whales	16

Page 18 is about _____

Page 28 is about _____

Page 16 is about _____

Page 8 is about _____

Page 12 is about _____

Apes are on page _____

Sharks are on page _____

Kangaroos are on page _____

Giraffes are on page _____

Chimpanzees are on page _____

Which page would you like to read? _____

Why? _____

Note for parent: Using an index is an important skill.

Second chance

Write the first two letters.

Connect two pictures that start in the same way.

Note for parent: This page gives children a chance to remember what they have learned.

Making lists

Write the words in the correct lists.

Things I use in the kitchen:	Things I use in the yard:

shovel

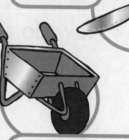
pan

knife

wheelbarrow

watering can

spoon

frying pan

pitchfork

food processor

lawnmower

Patterns in words

Make two more words by adding one letter.

ball   _all   _all

Write a sentence with each of the two words you have made.

1. _____

2. _____

Now do the same again.

man   _an   _an

hat   _at   _at

1. _____

2. _____

1. _____

2. _____

Note for parent: This activity encourages children to look for patterns in words.

Find the rhymes

Color in blue the words that rhyme with **take**.
Color in green the words that rhyme with **ball**.
Color in red the words that rhyme with **shell**.
Color in yellow the words that rhyme with **pin**.

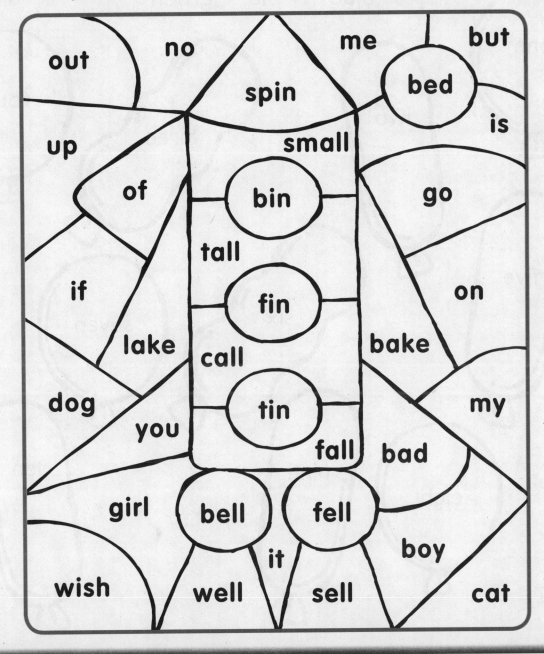

out
no
me
but
bed
spin
is
up
small
of
bin
go
tall
if
fin
on
lake
call
bake
dog
tin
my
you
fall
bad
girl
bell
fell
it
boy
wish
well
sell
cat

Note for parent: This activity helps children to see patterns
and to hear rhymes in words.

Number words

Color the balloons.

1 = red   2 = purple   3 = yellow   4 = blue
5 = green   6 = red   7 = purple   8 = yellow
                   9 = blue   10 = green

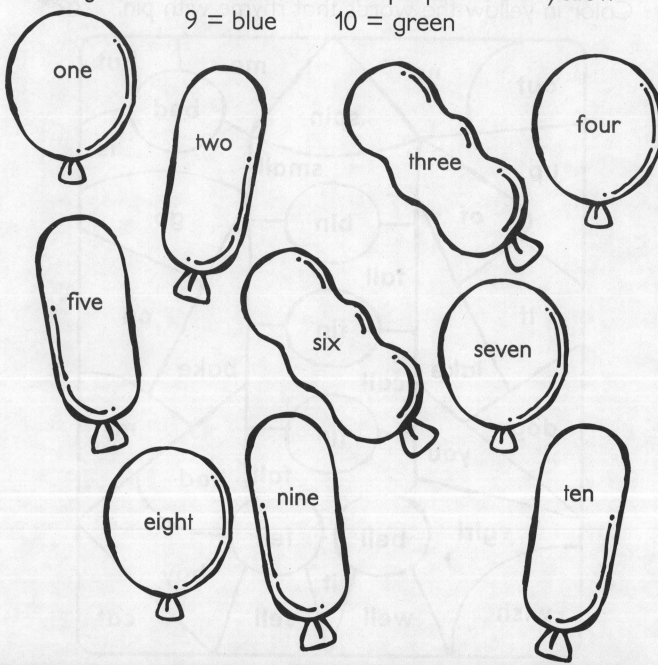

one

two

three

four

five

six

seven

eight

nine

ten

Word endings

Look at the first picture in each row.
Draw a circle around two pictures in each row that have the same ending as the first.

Note for parent: This activity encourages children to listen carefully to word endings.

All about nouns

Words that name people, animals, things, and places are called **nouns**. Read these sentences and draw a line under each noun.

The boy is reading a book.

The girl is watching television.

The dog is playing with the ball.

The man is cutting the grass.

Find another noun in each picture and write it below.

_____   _____

_____   _____

74

Note for parent: This activity helps children to learn about nouns.

Adjectives

An adjective tells you more about someone or something.

Choose an adjective to fill in the missing words in the sentences below.

cold   **windy**   **blue**

happy   **small**   **fresh**

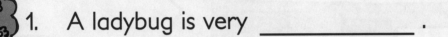

1. A ladybug is very _____ .

2. The leaves fell off the tree because it was

    _____ .

3. The sun was shining and the sky

    was _____ .

4. Dad had just picked the flowers so they

    were _____ .

5. The dog was _____

    because he had a new ball.

6. It was _____ in the park

    and there was ice on the pond.

All around you

Look at the picture. Words are missing from some of the signs and labels. Use the words in the box opposite to fill in the spaces.

Note for parent: This activity encourages children to learn about important words in their environment.

Café   Shoe store   Open   Trash
Main Street   Fish store
Bus stop   Mailbox   Telephone

In the dictionary

A **dictionary** tells you how to spell words.
The words on this page have incorrect spellings.
Look them up in a dictionary and write
them correctly.

fli
_____
fly

fog
_____

coot
_____

aple
_____

bred
_____

baloon
_____

lam
_____

pair
_____

qeen
_____

Note for parent: This activity gives practice in learning how to use a dictionary.

Dictionary skills

A dictionary also tells you what words mean.
This is called a **definition**. Draw a line to connect each
word to the correct definition.

	boy	A creature you read about in fairy tales.
	cage	A black and white bird that cannot fly.
	monster	A tool that has sharp metal teeth.
	saw	A male child.
	penguin	A pet mouse's home.

Now draw a picture for each word to
make your own picture dictionary.

Note for parent: This activity gives practice in using definitions.

Using verbs

A **verb** tells you what someone or something is doing. Check the verb in each box.

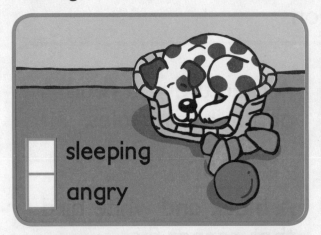

- [ ] sleeping
- [ ] angry

- [ ] happy
- [ ] licking

- [ ] running
- [ ] cold

- [ ] windy
- [ ] climbing

- [ ] dirty
- [ ] swimming

- [ ] flying
- [ ] fresh

What are you doing now? _____

Note for parent: This activity helps children to understand verbs.

Second chance

See what you can remember.

Read the words.
Write the numbers.

Connect each word ending to a picture.

two	
six	
three	
eight	
ten	
four	
seven	
nine	
one	
five	

 ce

 ake

 ing

 er

 ar

 tch

81

Note for parent: This page gives children a second chance to practice.

Months of the year

The second graders have made a chart to show when the children have their birthdays.

January	February	March	April
Solomon	Brian	Alison	Imran
Josh	Kate		
May	**June**	**July**	**August**
Ellen	Mark	Dale	Pat
Paul	Lisa	Kerry	Polly
Madison	Ahmed		Frank
Ben			
September	**October**	**November**	**December**
	Meena	Amy	Brendan
	Wendy		Connor
			Sally
			Gail

1. When is Amy's birthday? _____

2. When is Solomon's birthday? _____

3. When is Meena's birthday? _____

4. When is Dale's birthday? _____

5. Which month has no birthday? _____

6. Which months have the most birthdays? _____

_____

When is your birthday? _____

Note for parent: This activity helps children to practice the months of the year.

Fill in the blanks

Use these letters to fill in the blanks: **ai** (nail) or **ea** (meat). Read the words when you have made them.

p _ _ ch

l _ _ f

sn _ _ l

s _ _ t

s _ _ l

p _ _ l

Now use these letters to fill the gaps: **oa** (goat) or **ou** (house).

c _ _ t

m _ _ se

b _ _ t

cl _ _ d

r _ _ d

Note for parent: These sounds are not easy. Read the words in parentheses to help your child.

Descriptions

Look at the picture. Write a sentence saying what everyone is doing. Try to include a noun, a verb, and an adjective in your sentences.

_____

_____

_____

_____

Note for parent: This activity helps children learn how to describe people using proper sentences.

Compound words

You make a compound word by connecting two smaller words.

 +  =

horse   shoe   horseshoe

Now try to make compound words from the words below:

1. star + fish = _____

2. water + fall = _____

3. home + work = _____

4. play + time = _____

5. tooth + brush = _____

6. ear + ring = _____

7. book + mark = _____

Note for parent: This activity gives practice in making compound words.

Making new words

You can make new words by changing some of the letters in a word.

change the **p** in **park** to **m** = **mark**
change the **p** in **park** to **sh** = **shark**

Now try to make these new words.

1. Change the **b** in **bear** to **p** = _____
to **w** = _____

2. Change the **f** in **fire** to **w** = _____
to **h** = _____

3. Change the **j** in **jaw** to **cl** = _____
to **str** = _____

4. Change the **br** in **brown** to **cl** = _____
to **cr** = _____

5. Change the **fl** in **flight** to **br** = _____
to **kn** = _____

Note for parent: This activity helps children to understand the composition of words.

Reading for meaning

Three children have made a list of what they have in their lunch box. Read the lists and then answer the questions.

Kelly
turkey sandwich
potato chips
apple
chocolate cake
thermos of milk

Sam
bottle of water
piece of cheese
yogurt
banana
salad

Anna
yogurt
carton of juice
box of raisins
cheese sandwich
chocolate cookie

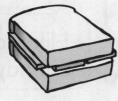

1. Who has fruit? _____

2. Who has yogurt? _____

3. Who has a sandwich? _____

4. Who has something made of chocolate?

_____

5. Who likes cheese? _____

6. Who has a drink?

_____

87

Quotation marks

Read what each animal says.

I like to fly and sing.

I have a long trunk.

I like to jump and hop.

I have a long tail.

I like to eat hay.

Write what each animal said using quotation marks.
Here is an example: Dog said, "I like to run."

1. Parrot said,   "_____"

2. Monkey said, _____.

3. Horse said, _____.

4. Kangaroo said, _____.

5. Elephant said, _____.

Note for parent: This activity gives practice in using quotation marks.

Missing letters

Sometimes when we talk to people we do not say every word.

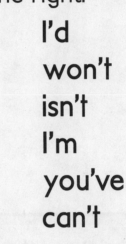

I am = I'm   It is = It's

Connect the words on the left side of the page to the smaller words on the right.

is not   I'd

cannot   won't

I would   isn't

I am   I'm

will not   you've

you have   can't

Write these sentences again using smaller words instead of the bold words:

I would like to see you but **I am** ill. **I cannot** go out but **I would** like to see you if you have time. It **is not** too far for you to come.

_____

_____

_____

_____

Note for parent: Explain how an apostrophe replaces the missing letters in these shortened versions.

Writing postcards

Write a postcard to a relative (such as your grandma, a cousin, or an uncle) telling them about your school.

Dear _____

Draw a picture that might be on the other side of the postcard, or cut out a picture and stick it here.

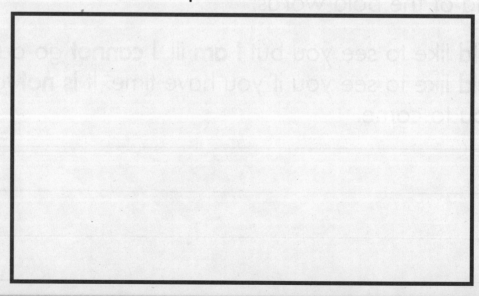

Note for parent: Postcard writing is good practice in an activity your child will recognize.

Speech bubbles

Look at what is happening in each picture. What do you think the people are saying? Write the words in the speech bubbles.

Reading instructions

Read the instructions and then draw on the pictures.

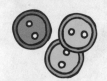

1. Draw a hat on the first clown.

2. Draw long shoes on the second clown.

3. Draw spots on the pants of the third clown.

4. Draw a flower on the hat of the second clown.

5. Draw curly hair on the third clown.

6. Draw a smile on the face of the first clown.

7. Draw a bow tie on the first clown and the third clown.

8. Draw buttons on the shirts of the second clown and the third clown.

Note for parent: This activity gives practice in following instructions.

Silly or sensible?

Some of these sentences are silly, and some are sensible. Read each one and then write the word **silly** or **sensible** beside it.

1. A library is a place to borrow babies. _____

2. Clocks help us to tell the time. _____

3. All boys have black hair. _____

4. Teachers like to teach bananas. _____

5. Cats have baby puppies. _____

6. There are a lot of animals at the zoo. _____

Now write two sentences yourself:

A silly sentence: _____

_____

A sensible sentence: _____

_____

Note for parent: In this activity, children can practice responding to different sentences.

Odd one out

Cross out the word that does not belong in each row.

1.	Monday	May	Friday	Tuesday	Sunday
2.	square	triangle	circle	shape	rectangle
3.	paint	red	orange	blue	green
4.	sheep	horse	pig	cow	lion
5.	bus	car	man	truck	van

Now put the words in the correct group.

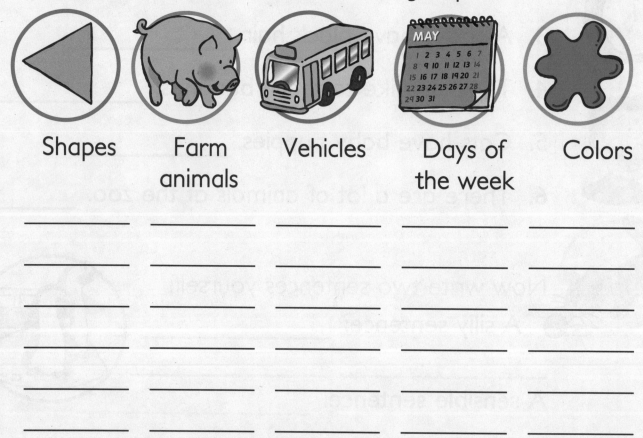

Shapes   Farm animals   Vehicles   Days of the week   Colors

Can you add two words of your own to each list?

Note for parent: This activity helps children to understand categories of words.

See what you can remember.

Make these words shorter.

is not   I would   cannot

_____   _____   _____

Sort these words into the three boxes below.

dog   tall   grows   soft   mouse
run   tree   cold   squeaks

nouns

verbs

adjectives

Note for parent: This page gives children a second
chance to practice.

Opposites

An antonym is a word that has the opposite meaning to another word.

big   **small**   **happy**   **sad**

Read the words in the box.

> pull   near   dry   cold   full
> hard   long   light   last   day

Use the words in the box to write the antonym of each word in this list.

1. wet _____

2. soft _____

3. first _____

4. far _____

5. empty _____

6. hot _____

7. night _____

8. push _____

9. short _____

10. heavy _____

Finish the sentences

Draw a line to connect the beginning of each sentence to the correct ending.

1. The dog barked   into the air.

2. The horse galloped   a big web.

3. The frog jumped   on the wall.

4. The birds flew   at the burglar.

5. The spider spun   across the field.

6. The cat slept   out of the pond.

Now finish these sentences.

The dolphin jumped _____.

The kangaroo hopped _____.

Word search

Look for these words in the grid below.

nouns	verbs	adjectives
dog	runs	fast
tree	grows	tall
mouse	squeaks	soft

a	e	m	c	i	g	r	t	h	j
s	r	l	c	b	t	a	l	q	k
d	o	g	s	g	r	o	w	s	z
f	k	f	m	u	e	s	b	g	s
d	g	s	t	t	e	q	n	q	u
r	u	n	s	u	f	u	d	m	p
p	x	a	l	j	y	e	u	o	n
w	f	l	o	o	v	a	l	u	t
y	a	z	e	v	n	k	y	s	b
t	h	x	a	e	c	s	w	e	d

Now find one of each letter of the alphabet and color each one red. There are 26 to find.

Note for parent: This activity helps children to recognize nouns, verbs, and adjectives.

A puzzle page

Make as many words as you can from the letters.

p	o	r
l	e	t
i	s	a
r	e	m

You can move in any direction but do not jump a square.

_____   _____

_____   _____

_____   _____

_____   _____

_____   _____

How many words did you find?

Change one letter to make a new word.

man   _____   You cook food in this.

coat   _____   You go on water in this.

card   _____   A horse can pull this.

fork   _____   Soldiers live in this.

wolf   _____   This is a sport.

Read and write

Color the words that you can read.

as	ball	came
down	eleven	first
girl	here	into
jump	kite	lived
much	name	once
people	queen	ran
she	this	us
very	water	x-ray
you	zoo	

Good for you! You have read a word for each letter of the alphabet.

Note for parent: The words on these pages are all high-usage everyday words for reading, writing, and spelling.

Write each of these words in the right group below.

Monday   yellow   three   green

Tuesday   eight   Wednesday   zero

Thursday   black   five   Friday

one   six   Saturday   two   ten

Sunday   four   blue   seven   white

nine   orange

numbers	colors	days of the week

Writing plurals

Plural means more than one of the same thing.
Make these words plural by writing **s** or **es** at the end.
The first one has been done for you.

switch**es**

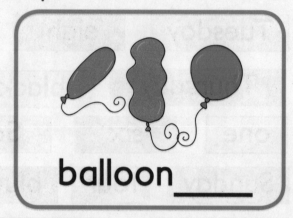

balloon_____

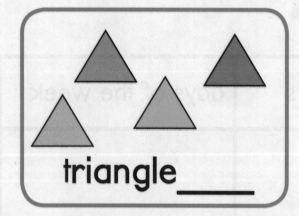

triangle_____

dress_____

glass_____

car_____

Note for parent: This page helps your child learn the plural forms s and es.

More plurals

For many words ending in **y**, you must take away the **y** and add **ies** to make them plural.

Write the plurals for these words. The first one has been done for you.

cherry

cherries

baby

lady

fly

pony

103

Note for parent: This page helps your child learn the plural form ies.

Spelling check

These words sound the same but mean different things. Circle the word that matches each picture.

 flower/flour

 which/witch

 son/sun

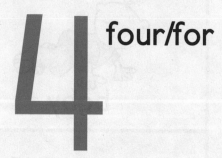 four/for

 bee/be

 bare/bear

Note for parent: Discuss some more examples with your child such as bean and been, sea and see, to and two, fare and fair.

Making new words

Can you connect two words to make a new word? Draw lines. Write the new words.

rain	glasses	rainbow _____
sun	bow	_____
butter	bag	_____
hand	fly	_____
horse	chair	_____
arm	shoe	_____

Note for parent: These new words are called compound words.
Ask your child if he or she can think of any other examples.

Word endings 1

Look carefully at the word beginnings and endings. Write each word in the correct place on the grid. (You won't fill all the spaces.)

ham   fan   bad   can   rat

map   sad   hat   lap   had

man   gap   ram   fat   Sam

	at	ap	an	am	ad
b					
c	cat				
d					dad
f					
g					
h					
j				jam	
l					
m					
n					
p			pan		
r					
s					
t		tap			
w					

Note for parent: After your child has completed the activity, they could try to think of examples to fill the empty boxes for extra practice.

Word endings 2

Here is another word grid to fill in.

cot	pill	bug	will	pen

hen	not	dash	bash	rash

rug	hot	fill	jug	men

	ash	en	ill	ot	ug
b					
c	cash				
d					
f					
g					
h			hill		
j					
l					
m					mug
n					
p				pot	
r					
s					
t		ten			
w					

Is it **ee** or **oo**?

Write **ee** or **oo** to complete these words.

b_ _ k

sh_ _ _p

ch_ _ _se

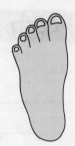

f_ _ _t

h_ _ _k

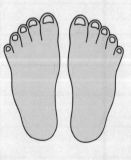

f_ _ _t

Note for parent: Say each word slowly and clearly, emphasizing the middle sound.

Write the correct word under each picture. Then write the words in alphabetical order in the boxes.

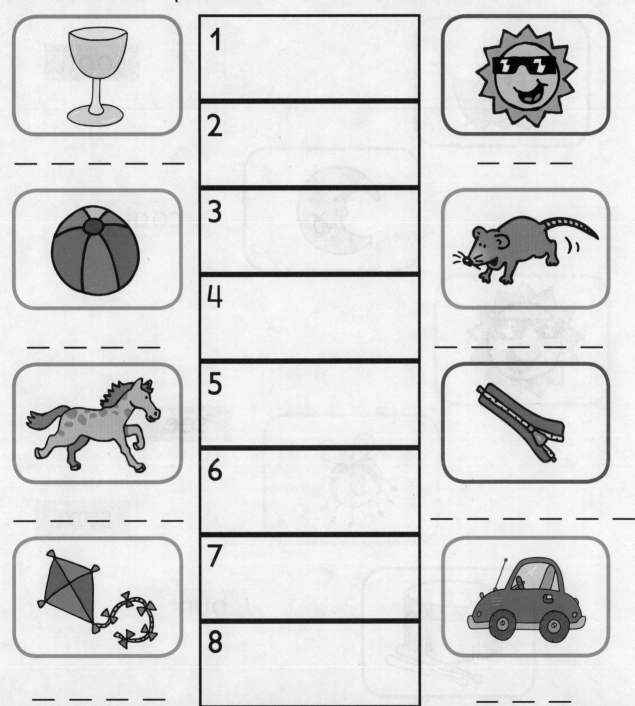

1

2

3

4

5

6

7

8

Note for parent: This activity gives further practice in placing words in alphabetical order.

Rhyming words

Say the name of each thing and draw a line to match it to a rhyming word.

soon

coat

see

sum

bun

Note for parent: Further practice with rhyming words helps build vocabulary.

Book titles

The books in this library need titles.
Make up a title for each book.
Write the titles on the covers.

Note for parent: When you read a new book with your
child, begin by discussing the book title and cover.

Finding words

Draw lines to the words you can make from the letters in the word **elephant**.

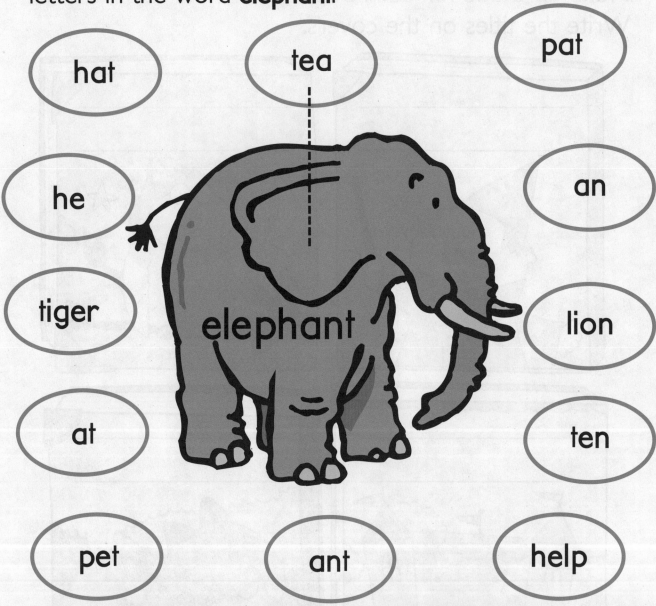

hat

tea

pat

he

an

tiger

elephant

lion

at

ten

pet

ant

help

Can you find any more words in **elephant**?
Write them here.

_____

Does it belong?

Read the words in each row.
Circle the one that is different.

| these | these | these | their | these | these |

| jump | just | jump | jump | jump | jump |

| took | took | took | took | two | took |

| much | much | many | much | much | much |

| way | way | way | water | way | way |

| than | than | than | than | than | three |

| how | how | half | how | how | how |

| after | after | another | after | after | after |

Note for parent: This activity gives more practice in reading
high-usage everyday words.

Count the letters

Count the letters in each word. Write each word in the correct box.

4-letter words

took

once

laugh

because

these

water

5-letter words

6-letter words

people

another

half

called

eleven

lived

7-letter words

Can you spell all of these words?

114

Note for parent: Writing a word reinforces knowledge of its spelling.

More rhyming words

Say the name of each thing and draw a line to match it to a rhyming word.

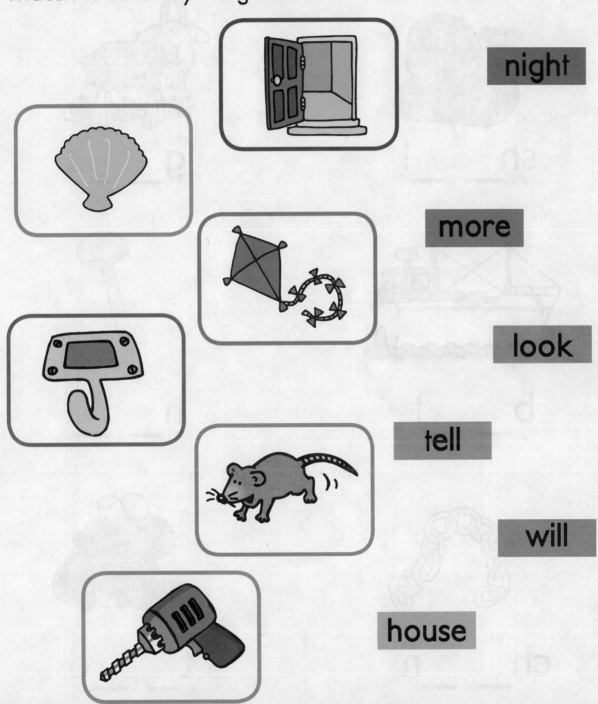

night

more

look

tell

will

house

Note for parent: Ask your child if they can think of any further examples of rhyming word pairs.

Is it ai or oa?

Write **ai** or **oa** to complete these words.

sn__ __l

g__ __t

b__ __t

n__ __l

ch__ __n

t__ __d

Note for parent: Encourage your child to listen carefully to the difference between ai and oa as you say each word.

Is it wh or ph?

Write **wh** or **ph** to complete each word.

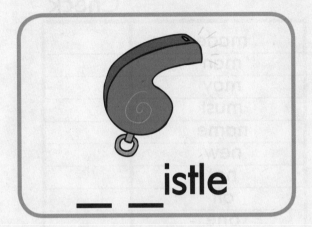

__ __ istle

ele__ __ant

__ __ eel

dol__ __in

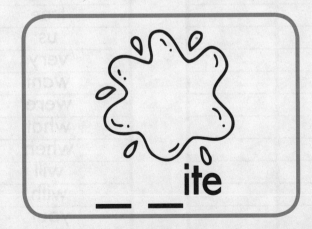

__ __ite

Reading checklist 1

Can you read these words? Check each one as you read it.

	Check
an	
as	
back	
ball	
be	
bed	
been	
boy	
but	
by	
call	
came	
did	
do	
down	
girl	
good	
got	
had	
has	
have	
her	
here	
him	
his	
house	
if	
last	
little	
live	

	Check
made	
man	
may	
must	
name	
new	
not	
off	
one	
our	
over	
put	
ran	
seen	
so	
take	
that	
then	
there	
too	
tree	
us	
very	
want	
were	
what	
when	
will	
with	
your	

118

Reading checklist 2

	Check
about	
after	
again	
another	
because	
brother	
called	
can't	
could	
dig	
don't	
door	
first	
from	
half	
help	
home	
how	
jump	
just	
laugh	
lived	
love	
make	
many	
more	
much	
next	
night	

	Check
now	
old	
once	
or	
out	
people	
pull	
push	
saw	
school	
should	
sister	
some	
than	
their	
them	
these	
three	
time	
took	
two	
water	
way	
who	
where	
would	

Answers

Page 12
dog, bed, cat, bus, pig, net, hat, sun.

Page 13
tree, flower, spoon, grapes, snail, clock.

Page 15
path, fish, swing, watch, duck, grass.

Page 16
2-letter words: do, be, us.
3-letter words: got, had, ran.
4-letter words: made, name, boys.
5-letter words: trees, house, girls.

Page 17

red
yellow
blue
green
orange
pink
purple
black
white
gray

Page 18
abcdefghi; ijklmnopq; mnopqrstu; rstuvwxyz.

Page 19

here	here	here	(have)	here
when	when	(were)	when	when
boy	boy	boy	(by)	boy
girl	(got)	girl	girl	girl
house	house	house	(had)	house
that	(there)	that	that	that
(made)	man	man	man	man
name	name	name	name	(not)

Page 20
snail, bee, wall.

Page 22
b: ball, bed, but; **h:** has, him, her;
o: over, one, off; **w:** what, want, with.

Page 23
mice–dice; ball–bell; bed–red; dog–log; star–car.

Page 26
log, fish, pen, bus, clock, pig, cat, bed.

Page 28

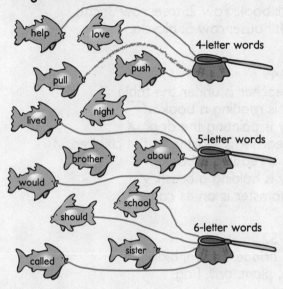

4-letter words

5-letter words

6-letter words

7-letter word: brother.

Page 30

night, cold, heavy, young, hard.

Page 31

yes ✔ no ✗

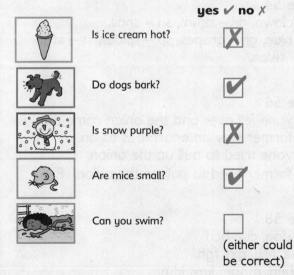

Is ice cream hot? ✗

Do dogs bark? ✔

Is snow purple? ✗

Are mice small? ✔

Can you swim? ☐
(either could be correct)

Page 32

yes ✔ no ✗

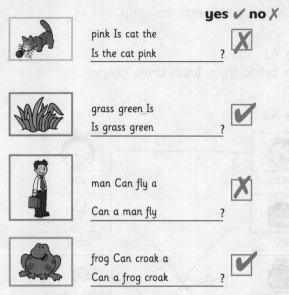

pink Is cat the
Is the cat pink ____ ? ✗

grass green Is
Is grass green ____ ? ✔

man Can fly a
Can a man fly ____ ? ✗

frog Can croak a
Can a frog croak ____ ? ✔

Page 34

cap/cape, fir/fire, cub/cube.

Page 35

these	these	(three)	these	these
many	many	many	(much)	many
half	half	half	half	(how)
water	(way)	water	water	water
after	(another)	after	after	after
than	than	(their)	than	than
two	(took)	two	two	two
called	called	called	called	(call)

Answers

Page 36
first, laugh, just, because, jump.

Page 42
drum, brick, frog, train, crab, grape.

Page 43

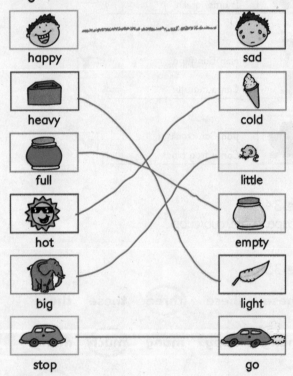

Page 46
dog, box, frog;
hat, bat, fan;
bell, web, bed;
sum, drum, bus;
six, pig, lips.

Page 47
man, red, pig, sock, jet, duck, bus,
bed, log, fish, crab, bell.

Page 48
Row 1: book; row 2: tree; row 3: cat;
row 4: house; row 5: bicycle.

Page 49
The teacher is under the table. ✗
A girl is reading a book. ✓
A boy is painting the door. ✗
The teacher is looking at the children. ✓
A cat is reading a book. ✗
A boy is holding a brush. ✓
The hamster is on its cage. ✗

Page 52
clock, bridge, crown, black;
green, plant, drill, flag.

Page 53
sp: spider, spoon, spaghetti;
st: stool, stamp, star;
sn: snail, snake, snowman;
sw: swan, switch, swing.

Page 54
cl – clown, dr – drum, sn – snail,
bl – blue, gr – grapes, sp – spider, st – star,
sw – swan.

Page 56
Everyone fell over and the onion came out. D
The farmer saw an enormous onion. A
Everyone tried to pull up the onion. C
The farmer tried to pull up the onion. B

Page 58
ball, dog, cat; bcd.
house, fish, girl; fgh.
ladybug, moon, key; klm.
rabbit, queen, parachute; pqr.
umbrella, seesaw, television; stu.

Page 59

or – fork, us – bus, an – man,
all – ball, am – lamb, in – twins,
at – bat.

Page 60

A little <u>girl</u> put on her dress.
The <u>sun</u> was hot.
I like getting into my <u>bed</u> to go to sleep.
I can see a bird's nest in the <u>tree</u>.
Dad kicked the <u>ball</u>.
A little <u>boy</u> put on his baseball cap.

Page 61

What time is it?
I like to eat chips.
When do I go to school?
The car was going fast.
Who went up the hill with Jill?
The cat likes to sit on my lap.
8 capital letters.

Page 62

Ashley, Joshua, Lily, Mya,
Noah, Olivia, Ryan, William.

Page 63

Wednesday, Saturday, Thursday, Friday,
Sunday, Tuesday, Monday.

Page 65

9827, 9026, 9146, 9544.
Ms. Walker,
Mr. Anderson,
Mrs. Todd,
Mrs. Depster.

Page 66

elephant :
A large animal with a long trunk and ivory
tusks. It lives in Africa and Asia.

kangaroo :
A large animal that can jump very well. It
carries its young in a pouch. It comes from
Australia.

monkey :
A small animal with long arms, and feet that it
uses like hands. It lives in jungles.

panda :
A black and white animal like a bear. It lives in
China.

zebra :
An animal like a horse with black and white
stripes. It lives in Africa.

Page 67

giraffes, penguins, whales, bears, turtles.
10, 4, 20, 18, 14.

Page 68

cl, br, cr, bl;
dr, gr, pl, fl.

spider>spaghetti
snake>snail
swan>swing
star>stool

Page 69

Kitchen: pan / knife / frying pan / spoon /
food processor.
Yard: shovel / wheelbarrow /
watering can / pitchfork / lawnmower.

Answers

Page 73

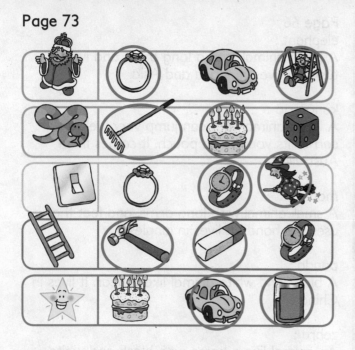

Page 74

1. The <u>boy</u> is reading a <u>book</u>.
2. The <u>girl</u> is watching <u>television</u>.
3. The <u>dog</u> is playing with the <u>ball</u>.
4. The <u>man</u> is cutting the <u>grass</u>.
Some of the nouns are:
1. sofa, lamp, mug, shoes.
2. slippers, book, chair.
3. tree, house, grass.
4. lawnmower, flowers, boots, hat.

Page 75

1. A ladybug is very <u>small</u>. 2. The leaves fell off the tree because it was <u>windy</u>. 3. The sun was shining and the sky was <u>blue</u>. 4. Dad had just picked the flowers so they were <u>fresh</u>. 5. The dog was <u>happy</u> because he had a new ball. 6. It was <u>cold</u> in the park and there was ice on the pond.

Pages 76-77

Page 78

fog = frog; coot = coat; aple = apple;
lam = lamb; bred = bread; baloon = balloon;
pair = pear; qeen = queen.

Page 79

boy = A male child.
cage = A pet mouse's home.
monster = A creature you read about in fairy tales.
saw = A tool that has sharp metal teeth.
penguin = A black and white bird that cannot fly.

Page 80

top: sleeping, licking.
middle: running, climbing.
bottom: swimming, flying.

Page 81

two–2, six–6, three–3, eight–8, ten–10, four–4, seven–7, nine–9, one–1, five–5.
er-ladder; ce-dice; ake-cake; ar-star; tch-watch; ing-ring.

Page 82

1. November. 2. January.
3. October. 4. July. 5. September.
6. May and December.

Page 83

leaf, snail, peach, seal, pail, seat.
boat, mouse, coat, cloud, road.

Page 84

Possible answers are:
Dad is playing with a red ball.
The baby is eating a big ice cream.
The brown dog is chasing the cat.
Mom is feeding the hungry ducks.

Page 85

starfish, waterfall, homework, playtime,
toothbrush, earring, bookmark.

Page 86

bear – pear – wear; fire – wire – hire;
jaw – claw – straw; brown – clown – crown;
flight – bright – knight.

Page 87

1. Kelly and Sam; 2. Sam and Anna;
3. Kelly and Anna; 4. Kelly and Anna;
5. Sam and Anna; 6. Kelly, Sam, and Anna.

Page 88

1. Parrot said, "I like to fly and sing."
2. Monkey said, "I have a long tail."
3. Horse said, "I like to eat hay."
4. Kangaroo said, "I like to jump and hop."
5. Elephant said, "I have a long trunk."

Page 89

is not = isn't; cannot = can't;
I would = I'd; I am = I'm;
will not = won't; you have = you've.
I'd like to see you but I'm ill.
I can't go out but I'd like to see you if you
have time.
It isn't too far for you to come.

Page 93

1. silly; 2. sensible; 3. silly; 4. silly;
5. silly; 6. sensible.

Page 94

1. May; 2. shape; 3. paint; 4. lion; 5. man.
Shapes = square, triangle, circle, rectangle.
Farm animals = sheep, horse, pig, cow.
Vehicles = bus, car, truck, van.
Days of week = Monday, Friday, Tuesday,
Sunday.
Colors = red, orange, blue, green.

Page 95

is not = isn't;
I would = I'd;
cannot = can't.
Nouns: dog, mouse, tree.
Verbs: grows, run, squeaks.
Adjectives = tall, soft, cold.

Page 96

1. wet–dry; 2. soft–hard; 3. first–last;
4. far–near; 5. empty–full;
6. hot–cold; 7. night–day;
8. push–pull; 9. short–long;
10. heavy–light.

Page 97

1. The dog barked at the burglar.
2. The horse galloped across the field.
3. The frog jumped out of the pond.
4. The birds flew into the air.
5. The spider spun a big web.
6. The cat slept on the wall.

Page 98

a	e	m	c	i	g	r	t	h	j
s	r	l	c	b	t	a	l	q	k
d	o	g	s	g	r	o	w	s	z
f	k	f	m	u	e	s	b	g	s
d	g	s	t	t	e	q	n	q	u
r	u	n	s	u	f	u	d	m	p
p	x	a	l	j	y	e	u	o	n
w	f	l	o	o	v	a	l	u	t
y	a	z	e	v	n	k	y	s	b
t	h	x	a	e	c	s	w	e	d

Answers

Page 99
Some of the words you can make are:
or, let, is, as, pea, at, mat, me.
man/pan; coat/boat; card/cart; fork/fort;
wolf/golf.

Page 101

numbers	colours	days of the week
three	yellow	Monday
zero	green	Wednesday
one	white	Tuesday
six	orange	Friday
five	black	Sunday
two	blue	Saturday
four		Thursday
nine		
seven		
ten		
eight		

Page 102
switches, balloons, triangles, dresses,
glasses, cars.

Page 104
flower, witch, sun, four, bee, bear.

Page 105

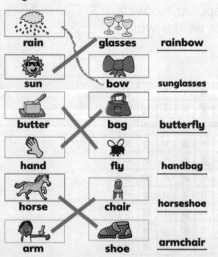

rain — glasses → rainbow
sun — bow → sunglasses
butter — bag → butterfly
hand — fly → handbag
horse — chair → horseshoe
arm — shoe → armchair

Page 106

	at	ap	an	am	ad
b					bad
c	cat		can		
d					dad
f	fat		fan		
g		gap			
h	hat			ham	had
j				jam	
l		lap			
m		map	man		
n					
p			pan		
r	rat			ram	
s				Sam	sad
t		tap			
w					

Page 107

	ash	en	ill	ot	ug
b	bash				bug
c	cash			cot	
d	dash				
f			fill		
g					
h		hen	hill	hot	
j					jug
l					
m		men			mug
n				not	
p		pen	pill	pot	
r	rash				rug
s					
t		ten			
w			will		

Page 108
book, sheep, cheese, foot, hook, feet.

Page 109
(In alphabetical order) ball, car, glass, horse, kite,
mouse, sun, zipper.

Page 110

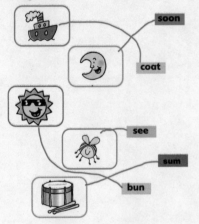

soon

coat

see

sum

bun

Page 112

hat · tea · pat · he · an · tiger · elephant · lion · at · ten · pet · ant · help

Page 113

these these these (their) these these

jump (just) jump jump jump jump

took took took took (two) took

much much (many) much much much

way way way (water) way way

than than than than than (three)

how how (half) how how how

after after (another) after after after

Page 114

4-letter words: took, once, half.
5-letter words: laugh, these, water, lived.
6-letter words: people, called, eleven.
7-letter words: because, another.

Page 115

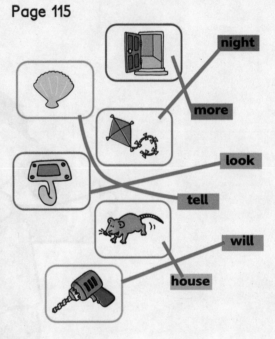

night

more

look

tell

will

house

Page 116

snail, goat, boat, nail, chain, toad.

Page 117

whistle, elephant, wheel, dolphin, white.